CW00406119

BIBLE STORIES

Four of the Greatest Stories Ever Told

Retold by David Borgenicht
Illustrated by Peter Malone

Running Press
Philadelphia • London

Canadian representatives: General Publishing Co., Ltd.,
30 Lesmill Road, Don Mills, Ontario M3B 2T6.
International representatives: Worldwide Media Services, Inc.,
30 Montgomery Street, Jersey City, New Jersey 07302.

Library of Congress Cataloging-in-Publication Number
93-85528

ISBN 1-56138-376-7

This book may be ordered by mail from the publisher
Please add $1.00 for postage and handling.
But try your bookstore first!

Running Press Book Publishers
125 South Twenty-second Street
Philadelphia, Pennsylvania 19103–4399

CONTENTS

INTRODUCTION

Using a small stone, a lowly shepherd defeats a giant warrior. A young man is sold into slavery by his brothers, only to find himself in control of their fate years later. A man finds himself adrift on a limitless sea, with the Earth's future in his hands. . . .

These are a few of the scenes in this book—stories of faith and betrayal, of love and war, of death and life. Here are four of the best-loved tales from the Holy Bible: "Adam and Eve," "Noah and the Great Flood," "Joseph the Dream-Teller," and "David and Goliath."

The retellings in this book are great stories. But they are more than that, for within them are truths that apply to us all. Each time we read or hear them, we come away with

something new and valuable—
strengthened faith, a greater love of
others, or the courage to face our
own giants.

ADAM AND EVE

from The Book of Genesis,
Chapters 1–3

In the beginning, God made the world and all that lived in it.

God made the sun and the moon and the stars. He made the rivers and oceans, the mountains and valleys, and the flowers and trees. He made the seasons and the weather. He created all the beasts that lived in the waters and upon the land.

And from the very dust of that land, God formed a man. He made this first man in his own image, and breathed life into him with his own breath. God placed the man in a plentiful garden called Eden. There, trees and plants grew full, flowers of every color bloomed like stars, and rivers flowed strong, bringing life wherever they ran.

The first man was called Adam. God told Adam that he was immortal, and would never die. Adam was to look after the garden for all eternity.

"You may eat from any tree in this garden," said God to Adam, "except one." God meant a huge tree in the center of Eden, which was covered in thick green leaves and golden fruit.

"That is the Tree of Knowledge," God said. "The day you eat that

fruit, you will grow old and will know the difference between good and evil. You will become mortal, and die." Adam said that he understood, and promised to live well.

So that Adam would not become lonely in Eden, God again molded the earth and breathed life into it. Wild animals sprang to life and birds burst into flight as God exhaled. The garden was vibrant, and full of motion.

But Adam was still lonely. Even though birds filled the air, fish swam in the rivers, and beasts ran through the fields, he was still the only person in Eden. He was still alone.

God saw this, and put Adam into a deep sleep. And while Adam slept, dreaming softly, God took one of his ribs. From that rib, God made the first woman, called Eve.

As Eve came alive, Adam awakened. "At last," he cried, "there is a companion for me in the garden!"

"And for me, as well," said Eve. The two of them smiled.

Although they were naked in the garden, Adam and Eve were not ashamed. They were innocent, and did not know shame. And after all, were not all the other beasts in Eden naked as well? Adam explained to Eve what God had told him about the Tree of Knowledge, and told her that they must never partake of its fruit. Eve said that she understood, and went off to explore her new home.

Smelling sweet blossoms and tasting juicy berries throughout the garden, Eve sat down beneath a large tree to rest. The gentle murmur of the wind in the branches pleased her, and she closed her eyes.

By and by, the murmur became a soft hiss. Eve opened her eyes slowly. There before her, dangling from the tree, was a serpent.

"Tell me," the serpent asked, "Is it true that God has told you not to eat from every tree in the garden?"

"We may eat from any tree in Eden except for the tree that stands in the center," Eve replied. "That is the Tree of Knowledge, and if we eat from it, we will someday die."

The serpent merely laughed. "You will not die," it continued. "Far from it. God knows that if you eat the fruit of that tree, your eyes will be truly open. He knows that if you eat that fruit, you will become a god with knowledge of good and evil, like Him." The serpent coiled itself near

Eve's shoulder.

Eve stared in amazement at the Tree of Knowledge, its golden fruit glistening in the sun. Her mouth watered at the thought of biting into the fruit and tasting its juices. What the serpent said made sense to her.

The serpent slithered back into the tree, and Eve got up. She went to the Tree of Knowledge and plucked a firm, golden fruit from its inviting branches. She smelled it, and it was the sweetest smell she had ever encountered. Immediately, she ran back to Adam.

"I have brought a wonderful fruit for us," said Eve.

"Where did you get it?" asked Adam, as he breathed in the lovely aroma.

"From the tree in the center of the garden," said Eve.

"We must not eat this fruit," Adam said. "God has forbidden it."

"God knows that if we eat it, we will become gods, too," Eve said.

"How do you know this?" he asked.

"A wonderful creature told me," said Eve. "A serpent, who is very wise. Now eat with me. Does it not smell wonderful? Imagine how it must taste!"

In truth, Adam could think of nothing else as Eve bit into the fruit. Eve gave the fruit to Adam, who ate as well. They both closed their eyes to savor the sweet, fulfilling taste.

After they swallowed, they

opened their eyes. They looked at each other and realized that they were naked! How could they have not noticed before? In shame, Eve ran behind a bush, and Adam covered his midsection with fig leaves. Now that they had eaten the fruit from the Tree of Knowledge, now that they knew of good and evil, of shame and innocence, they had become aware of their bodies. They both fashioned loincloths and turned red with embarrassment.

Soon, Adam and Eve heard God coming through the garden. Terrified, they hid behind a rock.

"Adam! Eve! Where are you?" God called.

Adam peeked from behind the rock, and arose. "We are here, Lord," he said. "We heard you, and hid in fright. We are almost naked, in nothing but loincloths, and we felt ashamed."

The Lord's voice boomed in anger. "Who told you that you were naked? Have you eaten from the Tree of Knowledge?" Adam and Eve bowed their heads.

"I only ate because she gave me the fruit!" Adam insisted.

Eve retorted, "And I only ate because the serpent tricked me into eating it!"

God's voice echoed like thunder through the garden. "Serpent," He proclaimed, "you are forever cursed. Because you have done this, you will crawl on your belly for the rest of your days."

"And as for you," God said to Adam and Eve, "because you have eaten the fruit which I forbade you to eat, you may no longer live in Eden. You will only eat what you can grow. You must work to find food. And only by sweat and toil will you survive."

Adam and Eve held each other tightly. "Furthermore," said God, "you will no longer live an eternal life. From now on, you are mortal.

You began as dust, and to the dust you will some day return." With that, he cast them from the garden, and ordered an angel to guard the entrance to Eden.

And so Adam and Eve left, to begin life in a world they did not know.

NOAH
AND THE
GREAT FLOOD

from The Book of Genesis,
Chapters 6–8

The world outside the garden was not as perfect as Eden. But it was fruitful and had its own beauties, and the people multiplied. Over many hundreds of years, they learned how to live on their own

without God's help. They learned to
build shelters, and to grow food.
They knew the difference between
good and evil. They shared amongst
each other, and lived well. And God
saw that it was good.

But then things started to
change.

People became greedy and self-
ish. They laid claim to the land, and
ravaged it. They killed animals and
each other without regard for life.
They betrayed each other, and

cruelty and violence were everywhere. God watched all this, and it made Him weep. He was pained that a world of such beauty—full of color and gentleness, full of such possibility—could also contain such wickedness.

"I must begin anew," said God. "But first I must find one good man and his family to carry on."

And God did just that.

In the world lived an old, wise man named Noah. He lived quietly

33

with his wife, his three sons, and their wives. Noah was the one good man of his time. He was neither wicked nor cruel. He had faith in people and in God, and he lived a godly life, helping those around him.

One day, as Noah was out walking, he heard a voice. "Noah," it said. Noah stopped. By the booming, gentle tone, Noah knew right away who was speaking.

"I have seen your actions and heard your thoughts," God said to

Noah. "You and your family seem to be the only kind people left. You are the only people who understand the precious gift of life. Most men and women in the world do not understand. The world has taken a turn for the worse. People have become heartless. They steal and deceive each other. So I must start anew."

Noah thought. He too had seen how people treated each other. But he did not understand what the Lord meant.

"Lord, what do you mean, start anew?"

"Soon," God explained, "there will be a great flood. It will rain for what seems an eternity. Water will pour from the heavens as if a huge spout has been opened above. Oceans, lakes, and rivers will rise up and drown the earth. The waters will destroy all that now lives, and the world as you know it will be gone. But I will save you and your family, because you have lived well. So you must prepare."

Noah looked up at the calm sky. Then he spoke. "What must I do?"

"Build a great boat," said God, "an ark that will float upon the rising seas, and carry you and those upon it to safety. Build many rooms within it. Seal the seams of the ark with tree sap to keep it from leaking."

"If it is just for me and my family," said Noah, "why do we need so many rooms?"

"Because it is not just for you and your family. You will take two of every animal aboard the ark with you. Take all animals that walk, crawl, fly, and climb upon this earth with you to keep them alive as well. They too deserve a chance to begin again."

Noah nodded. "I will do as you ask."

And so, though Noah was old, he worked day and night with his family to build the immense ark, just as the Lord had commanded. Noah and his sons had just finished placing the roof on the ark when the Lord spoke to him again.

"As always, you have done well, Noah. Now you must gather the animals together. Take them by twos—a male and a female of each. You have seven days—then the rain will come."

Seven days did not seem like much time to gather all the animals together. But Noah did as God asked. Two by two, the animals entered the ark, walking up a huge ramp Noah and his family had made. There was just enough room for them all. Most of the animals went calmly. There was a near-incident when the lions came aboard—they roared as they entered, frightening the gazelles. But Noah calmed them, and soon everyone was aboard. Even the elephants, big as they were, fit perfectly—and the giraffes, too, had enough room to stretch.

At the end of the seventh day it began to drizzle, just as Noah led the doves into the ark. They were the last animals to come aboard.

Noah held his hand out and caught the first drops. "The flood is upon us," he told his family. "We must enter the ark." Noah, his wife, and his sons went aboard, arm in arm. They paused only for a moment to take a last look at the land. Then Noah lifted the ramp up into the ark as the rain came down harder and harder.

The deluge began. The streams became raging rivers and the rivers turned into vast, stormy seas. The ark rode the torrential waters, rolling back and forth in the strong wind. But it never overturned.

It rained for forty days and forty nights. Several times a day, Noah went above deck to look for land, but he never saw anything but water.

The sun had disappeared. The oceans had risen over the mountains, first turning them into small hills and finally covering them completely. All that had once moved upon the earth, all that was not on the ark, was dead.

Although they were safe aboard the ark and had plenty of food, everyone became nervous. Even the playful monkeys seemed skittish.

"Surely," said Noah's wife, "we must find land soon."

Noah comforted her. "God will take care of us," he said confidently. Then he looked out over the prow of the ark. Nothing but water and more water lay all around them.

On the fortieth day, the rain stopped. The waters that covered the earth calmed—but they did not disappear. The sun shone, and the animals and Noah's family spent more time above deck. But they still floated alone on the waters, never coming to any land.

Each day, Noah sent a dove out from the ark, to search for a safe port. And each day the dove returned without finding a place to rest. But Noah had faith in God, and sent the dove out every day.

Noah stretched and awakened on the ark's 150th day afloat. He yawned, and listened to the waters lapping up against the sides of the ark. Then he got up just as he always did and went up to the dove's nest. He took one of the doves into his hands.

"Go and find land so that we can begin again," said Noah, gently urging the dove up into the air. Off it flew.

The ark was running low on food. Soon, they would need to find more, or they too would die. From time to time they thought that God had forgotten about them. But they dismissed such thoughts quickly, and went above deck to watch for the dove.

Blue was all anyone could see—

in the sky, in the water—just blue.
But the wind was calm, and the sun
was bright. It seemed like a good
day, somehow. And it was. Far off on
the horizon, where the ocean met
the sky, a tiny speck appeared.

Noah squinted, and his sons
leaned over the edge of the ark to
get a better look. The speck came
closer and closer.

"It is the dove!" Noah said.

It alighted on the edge of the
ark. In its beak was an olive

branch—a sign that land was some-where ahead. Noah laughed with joy.

"God will save us," he an-nounced. "Soon, we will reach land."

After seven more days, the ark had still not found land. Noah sent the other dove out to search. It never returned. Noah and his family went to bed disheartened.

The next day, Noah awakened as he always did, stretched and yawned, and went above deck. The sound of leaves rustling met his ears.

His eyes widening, Noah ran to the side of the ark and looked over. It had finally come to rest atop a mountain—and they were safe! Everyone embraced.

Noah lowered the ramp, and began leading the animals out. The scent of flowers filled the air, and Noah smiled, breathing it in. The world could begin again.

JOSEPH THE DREAM-TELLER

from The Book of Genesis,
Chapters 36–45

Joseph was his father's favorite son.

It wasn't that Joseph was better than his brothers, or that his brothers were cruel to their father. It was that Joseph was the only son of

Jacob's old age. To Jacob, Joseph was someone new to love—and in old age, new people to love do not come often.

Joseph's brothers saw Jacob's greater love for their young brother, and hated Joseph for it. So when Jacob made Joseph a beautiful coat of many colors, they hated Joseph even more.

One day, as they worked in the fields, they glared at Joseph from afar. "Look at him," said Simeon,

watching Joseph. "Strutting around like a peacock while we labor in rags. It's disgusting."

His brothers grunted in agreement.

"We should do something about our wonderful brother," said Judah. They went back to their work, jealous and angry.

That night, Joseph had a dream. In his dream, Joseph and his brothers were binding sheaves of wheat, preparing them for market. Because

Joseph had not been working the fields as long as his brothers, his wheat was bound loosely, and did not stand upright.

But in the dream, Joseph's sheaf arose and stood tall, while his brothers' sheaves fell down, as if they were bowing.

Joseph awakened confused. *What could the dream have meant?* he thought. Joseph got out of bed and went to tell his family what he had seen in the night.

Joseph's brothers laughed when they heard about his vision.

"Do you think you are better than we are," said Judah, "just because father likes you best? Do you think you will one day command us? Ha!"

Now they hated Joseph even more—for his dreams, and still more for telling them of his visions. They grumbled as they went off to the fields to work. And while they worked, they hatched a wicked plan.

"When he comes to the fields today," said Judah, "we should kill him, and throw him into a pit. Some evil beast will come and devour him, and we will be rid of him for good."

They all agreed. So they dug a deep pit, not far from where they were working, and awaited Joseph's arrival. The sun was hot.

Soon, Joseph came to them. "Behold!" said Judah, raising his hands in mock praise, "The dreamer approaches!" Joseph's brothers all stopped what they were doing, and mimicked their youngest brother. Then they grabbed Joseph. Before Joseph knew what had happened, before he could even cry out for help, his brothers stripped him of his beautiful coat and threw him into the pit.

Joseph's brothers sat down at the edge of the pit, eating their lunch, and discussing their plan. "What good is it," said Judah, "if we kill our brother and then conceal his death? We must make father think that Joseph has died by accident. And we must rid ourselves of Joseph's body. Father might discover it someday."

"What do you suggest?" asked the others.

"Let us sell Joseph to the Ishmaelites as a slave. He will never return. We can keep the money. Then we can kill a goat and rub its blood on Joseph's coat. Father will think he has been eaten by a lion."

Their mouths full of bread and wine, the brothers laughed at Judah's plan, and decided to do as he suggested.

After lunch, the brothers threw a rope down into the pit, and brought Joseph up.

"Thank you, brothers," said Joseph, "I knew you could not leave me to die." Then he saw that his coat had been covered in blood.

"What is this?" Joseph asked.

"It is the evidence of your

death," said Benjamin, laughing. Then they took their young brother to the slave traders. They sold Joseph for twenty pieces of silver.

"Not a bad price for a young boy like him," said Judah, jingling the coins. And the brothers then set off for their father's house to give him the bad news.

Jacob wept. His sons comforted him, but Jacob mourned for many days.

* * *

Many years passed, and because of a misunderstanding, Joseph found himself in a prison cell in Egypt. The Lord was watching over Joseph, though, and things were about to change.

One day, the Pharaoh's royal servant—who had once been imprisoned with Joseph—was taking breakfast to the Pharaoh. He knocked on the Pharaoh's bedchamber.

"WHAT!" grumbled the Pharaoh.

The servant was taken by surprise. Though he was very powerful, the Pharaoh was usually a calm, good man. He rarely yelled.

"I—I've brought breakfast, my Pharaoh," the servant said, his voice trembling.

"Oh," said the Pharaoh, "Come in. I am restless. I had a strange dream last night that disturbed me, and I cannot interpret it. I called all my magicians and wise men, but they were no help. No one can tell me what my dream means!" The Pharaoh banged the breakfast tray in anger.

The servant's eyes widened as he remembered the prisoner named Joseph.

"I think I know someone who may be able to help," the servant said. "In your dungeon there is a man named Joseph. Two years ago, when I was in prison with a baker,

Joseph interpreted the dreams that we had one night. Joseph told me that I would be released in three days, and I was. And he told the baker that he was to be hanged in three days, and alas, the baker was. If Joseph is still alive, he can tell you what your dream means."

The Pharaoh sent for Joseph immediately. The Pharaoh's servants bathed Joseph and shaved him. They threw away his ragged clothes, and gave him a beautiful new robe to

wear. Then they led him to the throne room, where the Pharaoh waited.

"My servant says that you can interpret dreams," stated the Pharaoh. "Is this true?"

"I cannot interpret them myself, Pharaoh," Joseph answered. "The meanings come from God. If you tell me the dreams, He will give the answer through me."

"It does not matter to me who gives the answers, as long as I have them. This is what I dreamed: I was standing by the banks of the Nile, when I saw seven cows come out of the river and begin to graze. They were well fed, and ate much.

"Then seven more cows came from the river. These cows were sickly and thin, and ate no grass at all. The seven thin cows ate the fat cows, but they still looked sick. And then I awoke.

"None of my magicians or wise men could help me," said the

Pharaoh. "Can you?"

"Yes," said Joseph. "The seven healthy cows mean that there will soon be seven years of plenty throughout Egypt and the surrounding lands. The crops will grow tall, and the people will have plenty to eat."

"That is very good," said the Pharaoh, beaming with joy.

"But there is more," said Joseph. "In your dream, the thin cows came up after the healthy cows and devoured them. That means that after the seven years of plenty there will be a great famine in the land. For seven more years, people will starve, and animals will die."

The Pharaoh looked worried. "What can we do? Can we stop it?"

"No," said Joseph, "but you can prepare by storing grain and food for the famine to come."

The Pharaoh considered this. "We will need an overseer to manage the storage—he must be a man of great vision and spirit—a man who walks with God, and is discreet and wise. A man like you."

The Pharaoh took off his ring, and placed it upon Joseph's hand. Then he summoned the members of his staff, who came swiftly.

"Dress Joseph in my finest linen robes, and give him a gold chain to wear. From this day on, Joseph will be my second in command. I am Pharaoh, but no one will lift his hand or foot in the land of Egypt without

Joseph's consent. Make it so."

And they did.

***

Just as the Pharaoh had dreamed, there were seven years of great harvest and growth in the land. The people lived well, and Joseph lived well among them. He married, and had two sons. He became well respected by the people, and was happy.

Then the famine came. The land was barren, and the Nile became nothing more than a trickle. Corn and grain would not grow, and many cattle died. The people of Egypt were ready for the famine, though, thanks to Joseph's preparations. They had more than enough food.

But the people from the lands outside of Egypt were not ready. The famine stretched all over the land of Canaan—all the way to Jacob's lands. Jacob was still alive, and his sons still lived with him.

Jacob looked out over his withered fields. "We must do something," he said, "or we will surely die. I have heard that they are selling corn and grain in Egypt, and that the overseer there is a generous man. You must go there, my sons, and see if he will help us. Take all our silver, and come back with food."

So Joseph's brothers made the long journey to Egypt. They went straight to the palace to meet with the overseer.

When they arrived, they saw a huge crowd. At the front of it was Joseph, rationing out grain. His brothers did not recognize him. Joseph looked out over the crowd and saw his brothers staring at him. He also saw that they had no idea who he was. When they sold him into slavery, he was a young boy of seventeen, but now he was thirty years old, and bearded. Joseph smiled as they bowed down before him.

"Where do you come from?" Joseph asked sternly.

"We have come from Canaan," said Reuben, the oldest brother. "The famine is terrible there. Our animals are dying. Our crops are barren. We desperately need food. Please, will you help us?"

Joseph stroked his beard. He was glad to see his brothers, but he wanted to teach them a lesson.

"I don't believe you," Joseph said. And with that, he turned away and went into his house.

He went straight to his steward, and said: "Bring those men here, and prepare a great dinner. They will dine with me." The steward left.

Joseph's brothers didn't know what to think when they saw guards approaching them. The captain came forward.

"The overseer has called you to his house," the captain of the guard said, his sword rattling. "Follow me."

Reluctantly, Joseph's brothers

obeyed. They could not imagine why the overseer wanted to see them in private. When Joseph's brothers reached Joseph's house, they washed and laid out gifts that they had brought for the overseer.

Joseph entered, dressed in fine white linen. "Ah, gentlemen," he said. "Come sit. Have you families? Have you a father?"

"Our father is Jacob," said Reuben. Joseph's eyes teared at the mention of his father's name, and he turned away to hide his face. Joseph was overcome with emotion, and had to excuse himself. He went off into a private chamber and wept. Then he wiped his eyes, washed his face, and returned.

"Serve the food," he ordered, clapping his hands. But Joseph did not join them as they ate. He was planning a test for his brothers. While they ate, Joseph went to talk to his steward. "Fill the men's sacks with as much grain as they can carry." Then he took his silver goblet from a nearby shelf. "Place this cup in the youngest one's sack."

The steward didn't know what Joseph was up to, but he bowed and did as he was told. The next morning, the brothers departed for Canaan. Joseph watched them leave from his balcony. His steward stood next to him.

"When they are a mile outside of the city," said Joseph, "take the guards and apprehend them. Accuse them of stealing my silver goblet, and search their bags. When you find it in the youngest one's sack, bring him back to me."

The brothers were talking about their good fortune when Joseph's steward and the guards overtook them.

"Why do you repay good by doing evil?" the steward asked sternly.

"We don't know what you mean," said Judah.

"The overseer says that one of you stole his silver cup." He looked at their sacks accusingly. "I will search your sacks," said the steward. "And the one who is found with the cup will become the master's slave."

"Whatever you want," said Judah, opening his arms and beckoning. "Lower your sacks, brothers," he said.

They did. The steward and his men searched each sack one by one. They searched Benjamin's sack last.

As it fell open, silver gleamed in the sun.

"Behold, the goblet!" said the steward, holding it up for all to see. The brothers were aghast—none more so than Benjamin, who insisted that he had not taken it.

"The evidence would suggest otherwise, my friend," said the steward. He took Benjamin into custody and headed back to the city. The brothers could not let Benjamin go alone, so they followed closely behind. When they reached Joseph's house, they went back inside and fell to their knees before the overseer.

Joseph spoke without mercy. "How could you do this to me! You should have known that a man as powerful as I could discover your crime."

His brothers pleaded for mercy. "How can we prove our innocence to you?" begged Judah.

"There is no innocence to prove," said Joseph. "The one who

was found with the cup will remain as my slave. The rest of you may return to your father."

Judah stood up, and spoke. "Please do not be angry with us. We are your servants, and will do whatever you wish. But do not take our youngest brother from us. My father has already lost one son. It will kill him if he loses another. He still weeps for the loss of the first. We beg for your mercy. Let me remain here as your slave. I promised our father Jacob that I would watch over Benjamin, and my father will die of anguish if he does not return." With that, Judah fell at Joseph's feet.

Joseph wanted to be stern. He wanted to teach his brothers a lesson. But when he saw the tears well up in his brothers' eyes, when he saw the love they had for each other, and for their father, he could stand it no longer. Joseph began to weep. For despite everything that had happened, Joseph found that he still loved his family.

He spoke with emotion: "I am your brother Joseph! I am the one you sold into slavery! It is I, my brothers!" Joseph spoke joyfully, but his brothers could not speak. "Come closer, and look. I am older, to be sure. I am wiser, perhaps. But I am your brother and you are mine."

When they saw his eyes close up, they believed—and they cried, too.

"Forgive us, Joseph, for what we did to you," cried Judah, hugging Joseph.

Joseph smiled, and looked Judah in the face. "Do not punish yourselves for what you did to me. It was God's plan—he sent me to Egypt through you, so that I could help people survive the famine. So that I could help my family survive."

He went to Benjamin and took him in his arms. Then they all gathered together, in a great circle, and rejoiced in their reunion. Joseph's steward had heard everything that happened. He ran to tell the Pharaoh, and when the Pharaoh heard that Joseph's brothers had come, he was pleased.

The Pharaoh went to Joseph and thanked him for all he had done for Egypt. "But now you must go with your family," he said. "I will give you the best land in all of Egypt, and provide for you during the years of famine still to come. Go with your brothers. Go and see your father."

It was a joyful journey back to Canaan. The roads became more and more familiar to Joseph as he drew close to home. Even after the passing of years, things had changed little.

Jacob saw his children coming from a long way off. But they were with someone new. As they came closer, Jacob got a better look at the visitor. He did not really know him, but something seemed familiar. Even though Jacob's old eyes had begun to fail him, this visitor definitely seemed familiar.

When they arrived at the house, Jacob embraced his sons. "Welcome home," he said. "Who have you brought with you?"

"Just look closely," said Joseph.

Jacob went up to Joseph, and looked him over closely. "Jo— Joseph? JOSEPH!" He hugged his son. "I thought you were dead!"

Joseph hugged his father back,

tightly. "It's a long story, father. And we'll have plenty of time to tell it." He smiled at his family. It was good to be home.

David
and
Goliath

from The First
Book of Samuel,
Chapters 16 and 17

David was a good Israelite shepherd, and a good harp player, to be sure. He was brave and wise for a youth, that was certain, and had excellent aim with a slingshot. But he had no knowledge of battle. He owned no armor. He didn't even have a sword. And yet it was David who faced the giant Goliath, the mighty Philistine warrior who terrified the Israelites.

The war between the Israelites and the Philistines had been difficult and bloody. Many men had been lost, and the armies were both weary.

The Israelites and the Philistines were preparing for a final battle in the valley of E'lah. The Philistine army set up camp on a mountain

next to the valley. The Israelites prepared for the battle in a mountain camp across from them. Both armies rallied their forces for a mighty battle that would come any day.

But the Philistines had a secret weapon. They brought a champion from Gath for the final battle—a giant warrior named Goliath. Goliath was more than nine feet tall. The huge bronze helmet atop his head was big enough to hold three gallons of wine. The coat of chain mail

armor he wore weighed more than two hundred pounds, but he wore it as if it were a light robe. A sword more than five feet long hung from his belt, and he carried a fifteen-foot spear. Goliath was the strongest, fiercest warrior anyone had ever seen.

In his camp, Saul, the king of Israel, was having troubles. Saul was tormented by fits of rage and depression. He had nightmares that would not go away. Nothing seemed to be able to cheer him. It seemed that the spirit of the Lord had left him. Something had to be done to gain back the Lord's favor, or the Israelites would surely lose the battle that was to come.

One of Saul's servants came to him as he sat in his tent, his head in his hands.

"We can't stand to see you like this, my lord," said the servant.

"Nothing can be done," said Saul. "My men are tired. My mind stays awake, even as I sleep, and I cannot rest. Just leave me alone."

The servant hung his head and spoke. "We must start simply, my king. Perhaps—perhaps if we found a harpist, his music would pick up our spirits."

Saul paused. He rubbed his head, and scratched his chin. "You might be right. Find me a skillful harpist, and call him to me."

"I know just the man," said the servant. "Jesse of Bethlehem, a shepherd, has a young son who is a masterful harpist."

"Call him forth," said Saul.

So the servant sent for David.

Saul liked David immediately. His harp playing was beautiful and inspiring. But there was something more. David had a commanding presence. When he spoke, everyone listened. When he moved, people followed. His youth and vigor began to lift the spirits of the battered Israelites.

When David played his harp, Saul's nightmares went away as if by magic. "There is something special about that boy," said Saul. "We need him around." And so Saul made David his armor bearer.

Indeed, there was something special about David, for the Lord had chosen him to be the next king of Israel. But no one knew this. For now, David had just been made Saul's armor-bearer, and he went home to tell his father the good news.

While David was home with his father, the Philistines decided that it was time to reveal their secret weapon. So one hot day, an incredible sight appeared in the middle of the valley.

It was Goliath. He stood in the center of the valley and called to the Israelites. "Today, I defy the ranks of the Israelite army. Indeed, I defy all armies. Why should we fight huge battles and lose hundreds of men? This battle will be different."

The Israelites listened in their ranks, their mouths agape at Goliath's size. Goliath continued. "I propose that this not be a battle of many men. I challenge one man—any man you choose—to a battle to the death. If he kills me, all the Philistines will become your servants. But if I kill him, you shall become our slaves. That is how the battle will be fought. I await your champion." Goliath sat down on a huge boulder in the center of the valley, his bronze helmet glinting in the sun for all the Israelites to see.

Saul and his army were terrified. Never had they seen a man so huge! He could kill even their greatest soldier with ease. That was, of course, if Saul could persuade any of his men to fight the giant. And he couldn't.

The giant sat in the valley for days, awaiting a challenger. No one came to fight him. The battle would continue as before—army against army. The Israelite army was smaller, and seemed doomed to defeat.

On the morning that the battle was to take place, David returned to Saul. He had just reached the out- skirts of the camp when he heard the Israelites shout their battle cry. Down in the valley he could see the Israelites and the Philistines taking position for the battle. Hoping to find his brothers who had joined Saul's army, David rushed to the Israelite lines.

There David saw a huge man come to the front of the Philistine troops. The giant spoke. "This is your last chance, Israelites. Are you so weak and terrified of me? Are you so cowardly as to think that none of you can beat me? I give you one final chance to stop the bloodshed that will come. Send me your champion, and we will fight to the death. Otherwise, you all die."

David turned to the Israelites. "Do you see how this man insults us, the army of God?" No one spoke. "Does no one care about the mockery he makes of us?" The soldiers hung their heads in shame. "Well, I am no warrior. I am younger than all of you, and weaker. But I am not afraid to sacrifice myself for the people of Israel. I will fight this giant."

Eliab, David's brother, laughed. "Who do you think you are, younger brother? You who came here not to fight, but to watch the battle. You are arrogant and too young. War is for men, not boys. Go and tend your sheep."

One of Saul's men heard David's proclamation, and told Saul what David had said. Saul sent for David immediately.

"Do not lose courage, your majesty," said David, entering Saul's tent. "I am your servant, and I will fight the Philistine."

Saul turned and looked David in the eyes. "You cannot fight the giant.

You are but a mere youth. Goliath has been a warrior since before you were born."

But David would not take no for an answer. "When I was younger, I kept watch over my father's sheep. Whenever a beast came to attack the flock, I went after it. When a prowling lion grabbed a sheep in his jaws, I tackled him and rescued the sheep from his mouth. I will deal with the giant in the same way, for he has insulted the army of God."

"I don't know what to think," said Saul. "Aren't you afraid?"

David stood firm. "No, for the Lord will keep me safe."

"As you wish," said Saul. "Go and fight the giant. And may the Lord be with you."

David left Saul, and went to a nearby stream. There he selected five small stones and placed them in a bag at his hip. Then, with his sling-shot in one hand and his shepherd's staff in the other, David went to meet Goliath.

Goliath thought that perhaps he had been in the sun too long when he saw the boy walking toward him. Not only was he half his size, but he wore no armor. Goliath laughed out loud when David approached. David stopped and stood silently, surveying his opponent.

Goliath grunted. "By my gods, I will destroy you," he said. "Come to me and I will leave you dead for the vultures and jackals to eat—whenever they want a small snack."

But David did not turn back. He held his staff proudly. "You come against me with your mighty sword and spear. You protect yourself from me with your vast shield. But I come against you in the name of Israel, and with the protection of almighty God. Today, the Lord will deliver you into my hands. I will strike you down. And I will do it so that all the world may know there is a God in Israel."

Angered by the young man's arrogance, Goliath arose and moved toward David. David moved forward as well.

The giant removed his huge sword from its scabbard. It was almost as tall as David. But still David advanced. Goliath saw the young man lay down his staff,and place his hand in his small bag.

David removed one of the

stones and placed it in his sling. Goliath shouted, and charged with his sword high in the air. Swinging the sling around his head, David hurled the stone toward Goliath.

The stone flew through the air and met Goliath halfway. It struck Goliath in the forehead, and remained there. Goliath fell onto the ground, face down.

As the giant lay there, David cut off his head with Goliath's own sword. The Philistines took flight when they saw that their mighty champion had been defeated. The Israelites cheered, and pursued them. They had won the final battle.

The giant was beaten, and the war had been won. And all because of a young shepherd, his sling, and his faith.

This book has been bound using handcraft methods, and Smyth-sewn to ensure durability.

The stories were adapted from the King James Bible.

The dust jacket was designed by Toby Schmidt.

The interior was designed by Stephanie Longo.

The text was set in Minister by Richard Conklin.

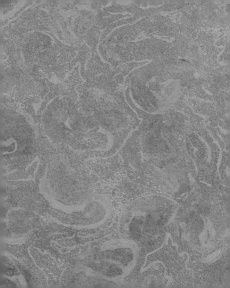